Dis. Pinocchio

LEVEL 3

Re-told by: Melanie Williams
Series Editor: Melanie Williams

Pearson Education Limited
Edinburgh Gate, Harlow,
Essex CM20 2JE, England
and Associated Companies throughout the world.

ISBN: 978-1-4082-8861-0

This edition first published by Pearson Education Ltd 2012

9 10 8

Text copyright © Pearson Education Ltd 2012
Copyright © 2012 Disney Enterprises, Inc. All rights reserved.

The moral rights of the author have been asserted
in accordance with the Copyright Designs and Patents Act 1988

Set in 17/21pt OT Fiendstar
Printed in China
SWTC/08

Published by Pearson Education Ltd.

For a complete list of the titles available in the Pearson English Kids Readers series, please go to
www.pearsonenglishkidsreaders.com. Alternatively, write to your local Pearson Education office or to
Pearson English Readers Marketing Department, Pearson Education, Edinburgh Gate, Harlow, Essex CM202JE, England.

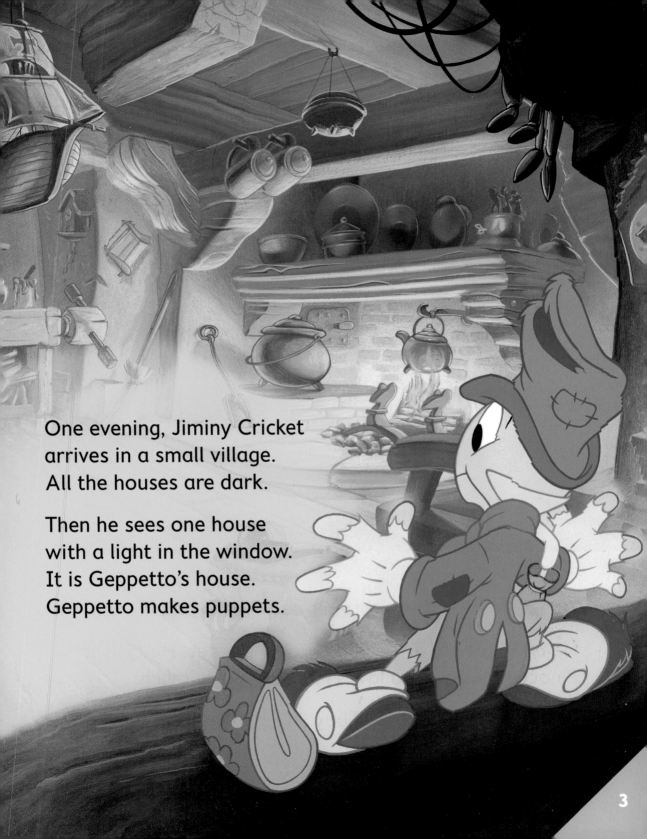

One evening, Jiminy Cricket arrives in a small village. All the houses are dark.

Then he sees one house with a light in the window. It is Geppetto's house. Geppetto makes puppets.

Geppetto lives there with his cat, Figaro and his fish, Cleo.

He is drawing a mouth on his new puppet. He calls it Pinocchio. Geppetto loves Pinocchio very much.

"I'd like you to be a real boy," Geppetto says.

Okay!

That night, a fairy comes into
Geppetto's house.

"Wake up, Pinocchio!" says the Blue Fairy.

Pinocchio opens his eyes. He can move.
He can walk. He can talk.

"Jiminy Cricket," the Blue Fairy says,
"please help Pinocchio."

"Okay!" says Jiminy.

In the morning, Geppetto is very happy. Pinocchio can move and walk and talk.

"Now Pinocchio, it's time for school," Geppetto says.

"Goodbye, Father," says Pinocchio.

"Goodbye, Son," says Geppetto.

Pinocchio runs after the children.

But where is Jiminy?

Honest John and Giddy see Pinocchio.

"Look," says Honest John. "That puppet doesn't have strings! Let's sell him to Stromboli. We can make a lot of money!"

Pinocchio does not go to school. He goes to work for Stromboli!

But Stromboli is not a kind man. He puts Pinocchio in a cage.

At night Pinocchio is very afraid.

"Oh, Jiminy, please help me. Where are you?"

"Here I am," says Jiminy.

"I'm here too," says the Blue Fairy. "What happened?"

"There were two big monsters ...," says Pinocchio.
"Oh! My nose is getting longer."

"That's because your story isn't true," says the fairy.

Pinocchio wants to tell the real story. The fairy makes his nose smaller.

She opens the cage.

"Let's go home," says Jiminy Cricket.
"I can run faster than you."

But Pinocchio meets Honest John and Giddy again.

"How about a vacation to Pleasure Island?" asks
Honest John.

"No ..." says Pinocchio. "Oh ..., okay."

"Pinocchio, come back!" shouts Jiminy.

"This is the coach for Pleasure Island," says Honest John. "Have a great vacation!"

Pinocchio gets on to the coach. There are a lot of boys on the coach. They are all going on vacation to Pleasure Island.

"We're here!" shout the boys. "This is Pleasure Island. Let's have fun."

Pinocchio runs to play with his new friends.

He is very excited. "This is a real vacation," he says.

"Wait for me!" shouts Jiminy Cricket.

Pinocchio sees a boy. "Look at you!" shouts Pinocchio.

"You have a donkey's ears, a donkey's legs ... you *are* a donkey!"

"Hee-Haw," says the boy.

"Oh, no," says Pinocchio. "Look at my tail! What's happening? Jiminy, help!"

"Quickly!" shouts Jiminy. "This way. It's the only way out."

Pinocchio and Jiminy climb up and up to the top of the hill.

"Now jump," says Jiminy.

They jump into the ocean and swim away from
Pleasure Island.

"Father, Father, I'm home!"
shouts Pinocchio. "It's me."

But Geppetto is not there.

Suddenly, a bird arrives with a letter.

Jiminy and Pinocchio read it.

Geppetto tried to find Pinocchio and now he is inside a whale!

"I have to find him," says Pinocchio.

"Come on, Jiminy."

Pinocchio and Jiminy jump into the ocean again.
They look for Geppetto and the whale.

"Father, Father!" calls Pinocchio.

Suddenly, Pinocchio sees the whale. It is sleeping.

Geppetto, Figaro, and Cleo are inside the stomach of the whale. They are in their boat. They are all thinking about Pinocchio. And they are hungry!

They want the whale to wake up and eat some fish.

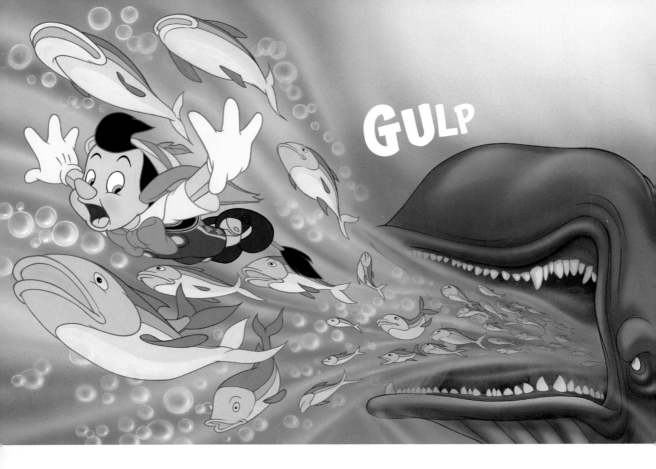

The whale opens its eyes. It sees a lot of fish.

The whale is hungry. It opens its mouth and swims fast.

"I'm not a fish!" shouts Pinocchio.

GULP!

Pinocchio is inside the whale.

"Pinocchio, it's you!" shouts Geppetto.

18

"How can we get out?" asks Geppetto.

"Let's make a fire," says Pinocchio. "We want to make the whale sneeze."

"Make him sneeze?" asks Geppetto.

"Yes," says Pinocchio.

They make a fire and get into a small boat.

Aaaaaa, Aaaatchoooooooo

The whale is very angry. It swims after Pinocchio and Geppetto. Pinocchio is afraid. He takes his father's shirt in his hand and swims to an island. He saves Geppetto's life.

But what happened to Pinocchio?

"My boy!" cries Geppetto. "You saved my life and now you are dead." He is very sad.

Then the Blue Fairy arrives. "Pinocchio, you were good," she says. "You saved Geppetto's life. Now you can be a real boy."

"Father, I'm a real boy," says Pinocchio. "Look!"

Geppetto looks at him. "You *are* a real boy!" he cries.

Geppetto, Pinocchio, Jiminy, Figaro, and Cleo are all very happy.

They dance and dance.

Activity page ❶

Before You Read

❶ Match the words and pictures.

ⓐ

ⓑ

ⓒ

ⓓ

1 a fairy
2 a whale
3 a donkey
4 a puppet

❷ This is a story about a puppet. Look in the book and find his name.

Activity page ❷

After You Read

**❶ Find these people or animals in the story.
Are they Pinocchio's friends?**

ⓐ Jiminy Cricket   ⓑ Geppetto   ⓒ Honest John   ⓓ Stromboli   ⓔ Cleo   ⓕ Figaro

❷ Read and write True (T) or False (F).

1 Geppetto makes puppets.
2 Jiminy Cricket is a cat.
3 Geppetto wants Pinocchio to be a real boy.
4 The Blue Fairy wakes Pinocchio up.
5 Pinocchio goes to school with Honest John.
6 Pinocchio's nose gets longer because he tells a real story.
7 Pinocchio grows a donkey's ears and tail.
8 Geppetto is on a boat inside the whale's mouth.
9 The Blue Fairy makes Pinocchio a real boy.

❸ Now tell the story with a friend. Use the pictures to help you.